JEWEL
SPIRIT

"WE ARE NOT
SEPARATE
FROM SPIRIT,
WE ARE IN IT"
Plotinus

Project Manager: Jeannette DeLisa
Book Art Layout: Jorge Paredes
Album Art Direction & Design: Brenda Rotheiser
Photography: Matthew Rolston
Calligraphy: Jeanne Greco
Nedra and Jewel Photo: David Drebin
Album Artwork © 1998 Atlantic Recording Corporation

Special thanks to Judy Stakee and Peter Galvin

**For more information about Jewel visit www.jewelJK.com,
or call toll-free 877-BYJEWEL (877-295-3935)**

I've had five incredible years of creating and living my dreams. I couldn't have done it without your support. Your enjoyment of my music, your prayers and encouragement have made all the difference to me. Most of all, the stories you have shared show such a growing hope and reveal your courageous hearts. This is, in part, what inspired me to create this album.
Thank you.

"CHERISH YOUR VISION; CHERISH YOUR IDEALS;
CHERISH THE MUSIC THAT STIRS IN YOUR HEART,
THE BEAUTY THAT FORMS IN YOUR MIND,
THE LOVELINESS THAT DRAPES
YOUR PUREST THOUGHTS,
IF YOU REMAIN TRUE TO THEM,
YOUR WORLD WILL AT LAST BE BUILT."
James Allen

YOU ARE THE DIFFERENCE

Living Spirit

My mother has always sought to understand what it means to be a human being in the highest sense and how to be that. She has gently inspired and nurtured that desire in me.

This album is dedicated to my mother and partner, Nedra Carroll, who is an example and teacher to me of what it means to be the difference and to all of you who are being the difference in our world.

PAGE 9 » DEEP WATER

You find yourself falling down » Your hopes in the sky » But your heart like grape gum on the ground » And you try to find yourself » In the abstractions of religion » And the cruelty of everyone else » And you wake up to realize » Your standard of living somehow got stuck on survive »» When you're standing in deep water » And you're bailing yourself out with a straw » And when you're drowning in deep water » And you wake up making love to a wall » Well it's these little times that help to remind » It's nothing without love »» You wake up to realize your only friend » Has never been yourself or anyone who cared in the end » That's when suddenly everything fades or falls away » 'Cause the chains which once held us are only the chains which we've made »» When you're standing in deep water » And you're bailing yourself out with a straw » And when you're drowning in deep water » And you wake up making love to a wall » Well it's these little times that help to remind » It's nothing without love, love, love » It's nothing without love » We've compromised our pride » And sacrificed our health » We have to demand more » Not of each other » But more from ourselves »» 'Cause when you're standing in deep water » And you're bailing yourself out with a straw » When you're drowning in deep water » And you wake up making love to a wall » Well it's these little times that help to remind » It's nothing without love, love, love » It's nothing without love » It's nothing without love »

PAGE 20 » WHAT'S SIMPLE IS TRUE

Turn to me with frozen lips » Your hands are icy cold » Your eyes burn bright against the frost-bit sky » You never seemed more lovely than you do tonight » Pale on the horizon » Like leaves frozen in the snow » Our two shadows merge inseparably » Will time stand still if it's pierced with cold » The more I live » The more I know » What's simple is true » I love you »» There's a warmth in my heart » It haunts me when you're gone » Mend me to your side and never let go » Say 'Time knows nothing, we'll never grow cold' » The more I live » The more I know » What's simple is true » I love you »» Twilight descends on our silhouette » How soon spring comes » How soon spring forgets » I wanna hold time, say it'll never begin » Old man winter be our friend » Old man winter be our friend » 'Cause the more I live » The more I know » What's simple is true » What's simple is true » I love, I love you »

PAGE 28 » HANDS

If I could tell the world just one thing » It would be that we're all OK » And not to worry 'cause worry is wasteful » And useless in times like these » I won't be made useless » I won't be idle with despair » I will gather myself around my faith » For light does the darkness most fear » My hands are small, I know » But they're not yours, they are my own » But they're not yours, they are my own » And I am never broken » Poverty stole your golden shoes » It didn't steal your laughter » And heartache came to visit me » But I knew it wasn't ever after »» We'll fight, not out of spite » For someone must stand up for what's right » 'Cause where there's a man who has no voice » There ours shall go singing »» My hands are small I know » But they're not yours, they are my own » But they're not yours, they are my own » I am never broken »» In the end only kindness matters » In the end only kindness matters »» I will get down on my knees, and I will pray » I will get down on my knees, and I will pray » I will get down on my knees, and I will pray »» My hands are small I know » But they're not yours, they are my own » But they're not yours, they are my own » And I am never broken »» My hands are small I know » But they're not yours, they are my own » But they're not yours, they are my own » And I am never broken » We are never broken » We are God's eyes » God's hands » God's mind » We are God's eyes » God's hands » God's heart » We are God's eyes » God's hands » God's eyes » We are God's hands » We are God's hands »

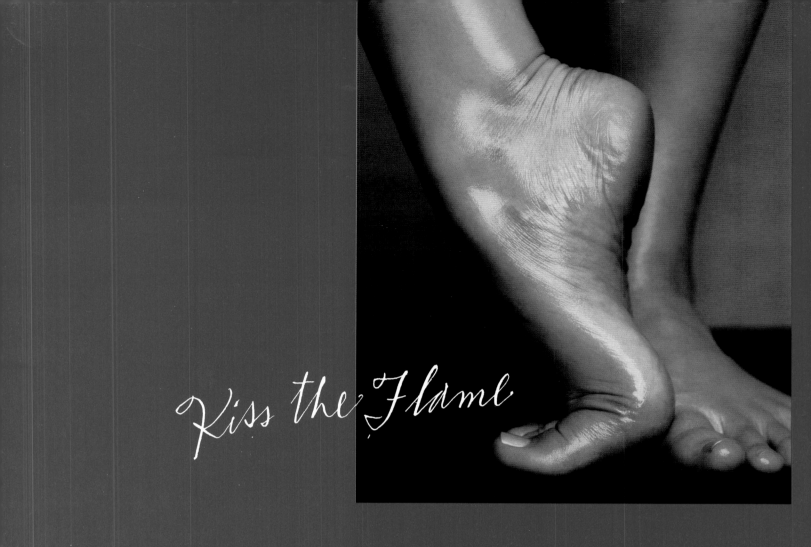

Kiss the Flame

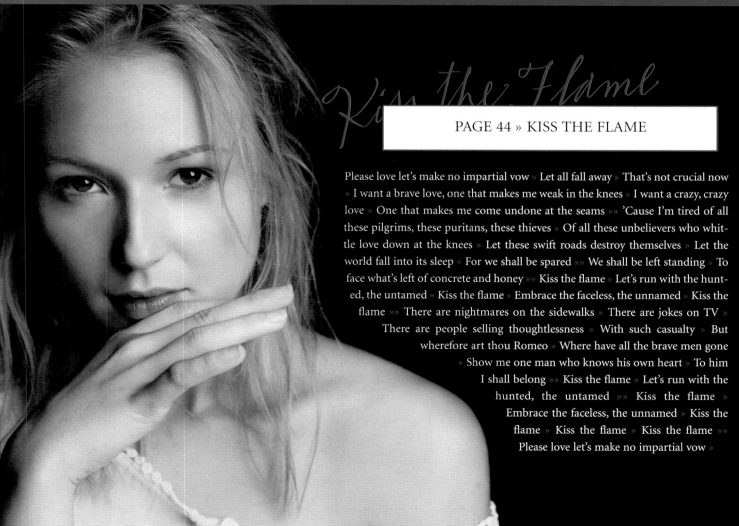

Kiss the Flame

PAGE 44 » KISS THE FLAME

Please love let's make no impartial vow » Let all fall away » That's not crucial now » I want a brave love, one that makes me weak in the knees » I want a crazy, crazy love » One that makes me come undone at the seams »» 'Cause I'm tired of all these pilgrims, these puritans, these thieves » Of all these unbelievers who whittle love down at the knees » Let these swift roads destroy themselves » Let the world fall into its sleep » For we shall be spared »» We shall be left standing » To face what's left of concrete and honey »» Kiss the flame » Let's run with the hunted, the untamed » Kiss the flame » Embrace the faceless, the unnamed » Kiss the flame »» There are nightmares on the sidewalks » There are jokes on TV » There are people selling thoughtlessness » With such casualty » But wherefore art thou Romeo » Where have all the brave men gone » Show me one man who knows his own heart » To him I shall belong »» Kiss the flame » Let's run with the hunted, the untamed »» Kiss the flame » Embrace the faceless, the unnamed » Kiss the flame » Kiss the flame » Kiss the flame »» Please love let's make no impartial vow »

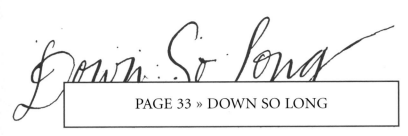

PAGE 33 » DOWN SO LONG

Sun sets 'cross the ocean » I'm a thousand miles from anywhere » My pocketbook and my heart both just got stolen » And the sun act like she don't even care » The wind blows cold when you reach the top » It feels like someone's face is stuck to the bottom of my shoe » I got a plastic Jesus, a cordless telephone for every corner of my room » Got everybody but you telling me what to do » But I've been down so long » Ooh, it can't be longer still » I've been down so long » That the end must be drawing near » I look to everybody but me to answer my prayers » 'Til I saw an angel in a bathroom who said she saw no one worth saving » anywhere » And a blind man on the corner said it's simple, like flipping a coin » Don't matter what side it lands on if it's someone else's dime » But I've been down so long » Ooh, it can't be longer still » We've been down so long » That the end must be drawing near »» I take a trip, I catch a train, I catch a plane » I got a ticket in my hand » And then a man takes my money » And like cattle we all stand » But we've been down so long » Ooh, it can't be longer still »» We've been down so long » The end must be... » I know the end must be... » Oh, I know the end must be drawing near »» Bridge Repeat / Scat Section

PAGE 50 » INNOCENCE MAINTAINED

Ophelia drowned in the water » Crushed by her own weight » Hitler loved little blue-eyed boys » And it drove him to hate » Birds always grow silent before the night descends » 'Cause nature has a funny way of breaking what does not bend » A hero's torso built of steel and Novocain » His heart a bitter beat inside a bloodless frame» There was a hole inside his soul a manicure could not fill » So he found himself a whore to love while daisies choked in the window sill »» We've made houses for hatred » It's time we made a place » Where people's souls may be seen and made safe » Be careful with each other » These fragile flames » For innocence can't be lost » It just needs to be maintained »» A small town in Ohio » Two boys are filled with violence » And darkness spreads its legs for hate and ignorance » We are given to a god to put our faith therein » But to be forgiven, we must first believe in sin »» We've made houses for hatred » It's time we made a place » Where people's souls may be seen and made safe » Be careful with each other » These fragile flames » For innocence can't be lost » It just needs to be maintained »» I want to live bravely and love without fear » I want always to feel the wings of grace near » We all will be Christed when we hear ourselves say » We are that to which we pray »» We've made houses for hatred » It's time we made a place » Where people's souls may be seen and made safe » Be careful with each other » These fragile flames »» We've built houses for hatred » It's time we made a place » Where people's souls may be seen and made safe » Be careful with each other » These fragile flames » For innocence can't be lost » It just needs to be maintained »

PAGE 60 » JUPITER

Venus de Milo in her half-baked shell » Understood the nature of love very well » She said, "A good love is delicious, you can't get enough too soon. It makes you so crazy you want to swallow the moon." » Oh, oh Jupiter » Oh, oh be still my little heart » Oh, oh love is a flame neither timid nor tame »» Take these stars from my crown » Let the years fall down » Lay me out in firelight » Let my skin feel the night » Fasten me to your side » Say it will be soon » You make me so crazy, baby » Could swallow the moon »» My hands are two travelers they've crossed oceans and lands » Yet they are too small on the continent of your skin » Wandering, wandering I could spend my life » Traveling the length of your body each night »» Oh, oh Jupiter » Oh, oh be still my little heart » Oh, oh love is a flame neither timid nor tame » Take these stars from my crown » Let the years fall down » Lay me out in firelight » Let my skin feel the night » Fasten me to your side » And say it will be soon » You make me so crazy, baby » Could swallow the moon » Swallow the moon »» Oh, oh Jupiter » Oh, oh be still my little heart » Oh, oh love is a flame neither timid nor tame » Take these stars from my crown » Let the years fall down » Lay me out in firelight » Let my skin feel the night » Fasten me to your side »» And say it will be soon » You make me so crazy, baby » Could swallow the moon » Swallow the moon » Swallow the moon » Swallow the moon »

Fat Boy

Fat boy goes to the pool » Sees his reflection, doesn't know what to do » He feels little inside and filled with pride » Oh, fragile flame » No one sees the same »» Fat boy goes about his day » Trying to think of funny things to say » Like, "This is just a game I play" » And, "I like me this way" » Oh, fragile flame » When no one feels the same »» Hush, sleep, don't think, just eat » Your daddy's little boy » Your mama's pride and joy » You know they love ya » But not because they hold ya »» Fat boy says "Wouldn't it be nice » If I could melt myself like ice » Or outrun my skin and just be pure wind" » Oh, fragile flame » Sometimes I feel the same »

Enter from the East

I went out a-wandering
Beneath an unknown sky
The heavens all shook violently
He caught my eye
Strange fruit fell
It struck me to the core
My heart became a single flame
It wanted nothing more
Stranger, enter from the East
Stranger, step inside this place
Oh, and own me, own me.

The clock became a bullet hole
Cruel and unkind
It hurt me with its second hand
Alone another night
Stranger, enter from the East
Stranger, step inside this place

Blue, is that you?
Well, don't bother knocking on my door this time
Blue, go be true for someone else
There's no room inside this heart of mine
My heart has four empty rooms
Three wait for lightning and one waits for you

I must have you all to myself
Feel the full weight of your skin
I'll hollow out my insides
To place you in
Stranger, enter from the East
Stranger, step inside this place
Oh, and own me, own me

Barcelona

Barcelona where the winds all blew » And the churches don't have windows but the graveyards do » Me and my shadow are wrestling again » Look out stranger, there's a dark cloud moving in » But if you could hear the voice in my heart it would tell you » I'm afraid I am alone » Won't somebody please hold me, release me » Show me the meaning of mercy » Let me loose » Fly, let me fly, let me fly » Super paranoid, I'm blending, I'm blurring, I'm bleeding into the scenery » Loving someone else is always so much easier » But I hold myself hostage in the mirror » But If you could hear the voice in my heart it would tell you » I'm tired of feeling this way » God, won't you please hold me, release me » Show me the meaning of mercy » Let me loose » Let me fly, let me fly, let me fly »» I won't be held down, I won't be held back » I will lead with my faith »» The red light has been following me » But don't worry mother » It's no longer my gravity » Hold me, release me » Show me the meaning of mercy » Let me fly, let me fly, let me fly »

Life Uncommon *Do You*

Absence of Fear

Little Bird

LIFE UNCOMMON

Don't worry mother, it'll be alright » And don't worry sister, say your prayers and sleep tight » It'll be fine lover of mine » It'll be just fine »» Lend your voices only to sounds of freedom » No longer lend your strength to that which you wish to be free from » Fill your lives with love and bravery » And you shall lead a life uncommon »» I've heard your anguish, I've heard your hearts cry out » We are tired, we are weary, but we aren't worn out » Set down your chains, until only faith remains » Set down your chains »» And lend your voices only to sounds of freedom » No longer lend your strength to that » which you wish to be free from » Fill your lives with love and bravery » And we shall lead a life uncommon »» There are plenty of people who pray for peace » But if praying were enough it would have come to be » Let your words enslave no one and the heavens will hush themselves » To hear our voices ring out clear » With sounds of freedom » Sounds of freedom »» Come on you unbelievers, move out of the way » There is a new army coming and we are armed with faith » To live, we must give » To live »» And lend our voices only to sounds of freedom » No longer lend our strength to that which we wish to be free from » Fill your lives with love and bravery » And we shall lead... » Lend our voices only to sounds of freedom » No longer lend our strength to that which we wish to be free from » Fill your lives with love and bravery » And we shall lead a life uncommon »

DO YOU

Hey, you say you like the way the cowboys tip their hats and say, » "How's it goin' ma'am?" » But you're never quite clear if their glares are sincere » Or really only just second hand » To you it's all roses, it's a lavender haze » The man is a marvel, but it's a shame about his brains » But that's OK » You say "He's got straight teeth and it's good sex" » You look to the sky » You look to the man » You claim innocence and not to understand » Or do you, do you? »» There's a big man wearing a white suit and patent leather shoes » He wants to take his monkeys to see the kids at the zoo » 'Cause the gypsy on the corner said, » "Hey, Mister you can't lose." » And it's your first day at the track » You feel that heat on your back »» We all want to find a way to beat the system » Find some rhythm in the madness »» Get down on your knees and pray » Say, "I'll do whatever you want, God » Just let me have my way" » Well will you, will you? »» Come on all you merry men » Rally your cry » Dance with the devil for tomorrow we'll surely » Hey, hey blow the men down »» You with all your cigarettes and cool stares » Filled with blank glares and loaded regrets » Just like the girls today with nothing to say » No more pigtails and pony rides » They're sophisticated » They sip on lattes » And have their eyes on a bigger prize » We shake our fists and say, "Well good golly we're mad » That God kills children with our very own hands" » We claim innocence and not to understand » Or do we, do we? »» Come on all you merry men » Rally your cry » Dance with the devil for tomorrow we'll surely » Hey, hey blow the men down » Blow the men down » Hey

ABSENCE OF FEAR

Inside my skin there is this space » It twists and turns » It bleeds and aches » Inside my heart there's an empty room » It's waiting for lightning » It's waiting for you » And I am wanting » And I am needing you here » Inside the absence of fear »» Muscle and sinew » Velvet and stone » This vessel is haunted » It creaks and moans » My bones call to you » In their separate skin » I make myself translucent » To let you in, for » I am wanting » And I am needing you here » Inside the absence of fear »» There is this hunger » This restlessness inside of me » And it knows that you're no stranger » You're my gravity »» My hands will adore you through all darkness aim »They will lay you out in moonlight » And reinvent your name » For I am wanting you » And I am needing you here » I need you near » Inside the absence of fear »

THIS LITTLE BIRD

"Listening to my mother sing this song to me as a child is one of my first memories."

DEEP WATER

Words and Music by
JEWEL KILCHER

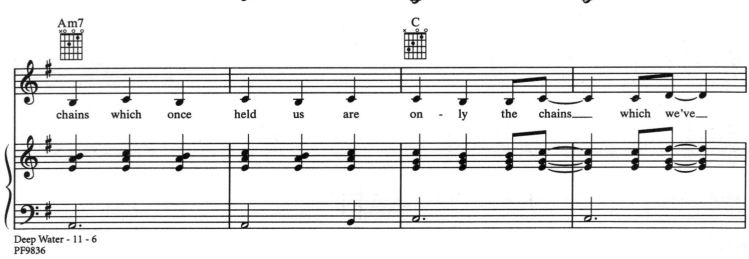

an - y - one who cared in the end._____

That's when ev - 'ry - thing

fades_____ or falls_____ a - way._____ 'Cause the

chains which once held us are on - ly the chains_____ which we've_____

Bridge:

love.

We've com-pro-mised our pride

and sac-ri-ficed our health.

We must de-mand more, not from each oth-er, but

WHAT'S SIMPLE IS TRUE

Words and Music by
JEWEL KILCHER

Verse 1:

1. Turn to me___ with fro-zen lips.

What's Simple Is True - 8 - 1
PF9836

22

Bridge:

HANDS

Words and Music by
JEWEL KILCHER and PATRICK LEONARD

1. If I could tell the world just one thing, it would be that we're all o - kay.
2. *See additional lyrics*

And not to wor - ry, 'cause wor - ry is waste - ful and use -

Hands - 5 - 1
PF9836

Verse 2:
Poverty stole your golden shoes,
It didn't steal your laughter.
And heartache came to visit me,
But I knew it wasn't ever after.
We'll fight not out of spite,
For someone must stand up for what's right.
'Cause where there's a man who has no voice,
There ours shall go on singing.
(To Chorus:)

DOWN SO LONG

Words and Music by
JEWEL KILCHER

My pock - et - book and my heart both just got sto - len,_____ and that

sun act___ like she don't e - ven care._____

Verses 2 & 3:

2. The wind blows cold_____ when you reach___ the top. It feels like
3. *See additional lyrics*

some - one's face is stuck to the bot - tom of my shoe. I got a,

I take a trip, I catch a train, I catch a plane, I got a tick-et in my__ hand,__ and then a

D.S.% al Coda

fat man takes my mon-ey and like cat-tle we all stand.__

⊕ *Coda*

end__ must be, oh, I know the end__ must be, oh, I know the

end__ must be draw - ing__ near.__

Verse 3:
I look to everybody but me to answer my prayers,
Till I saw an angel in a bathroom who said she saw no one worth saving anywhere.
And a blind man on the corner said it's simple, like flipping a coin:
Don't matter what side it lands on if it's someone else's dime.
(To Chorus:)

FAT BOY

Tune guitar: D-A-D-F#-B-D

Words and Music by
JEWEL KILCHER

Verses 1 & 2:

1. Fat___ boy   goes to the pool.
2. *See additional lyrics*

Sees his___ re-flec-tion,   does-n't know what___ to do.___ He feels

Fat Boy - 5 - 1
PF9836

Verse 2:
Fat boy goes about his day
Trying to think of funny things to say.
Like, "This is just a game I play,"
And, "I like me this way."
Oh, fragile flame,
When no one feels the same.
(To Bridge:)

KISS THE FLAME

Words and Music by
JEWEL KILCHER

Moderately slow half-time feel ♩ = 80

1. Please, love,__ let's make no im-par-tial vow.__ Let
2.3. *See additional lyrics*

all fall a-way_____ that's not__ cru-cial__ now. I want__ a__

brave__ love,___ one that makes me weak in the knees.__ I want a

PF9836

Please, love,— let's make no im-par-tial vow.——

Verse 2:
'Cause I'm tired of all these pilgrims, these puritans, these thieves,
Of all these unbelievers who whittle love down at the knees.
Let these swift roads destroy themselves,
Let the world fall into its sleep.
For we shall be spared,
We shall be left standing
To face what's left of concrete and honey.
(To Chorus:)

Verse 3:
There are nightmares on the sidewalks,
There are jokes on TV.
There are people selling thoughtlessness
With such casualty.
But wherefore art thou, Romeo?
Where have all the brave men gone?
Show me one man who knows his own heart.
To him I shall belong.
(To Chorus:)

INNOCENCE MAINTAINED

Words and Music by
JEWEL KILCHER

weight. Hit - ler loved__ lit - tle blue - eyed boys__ and it

drove him to hate.__ Birds al - ways__ grow

si - lent__ be - fore the night__ de - scends, 'cause

na - ture has a fun - ny way__ of break - ing what

Innocence Maintained - 10 - 2
PF9836

D.S. % al Coda

Hey,___ hey.___ Hey,___ hey.___

4. I

⊕ *Coda*

flames. We've made hous - es for ha - tred. It's

Verse 3:
A small town in Ohio,
Two boys are filled with violence,
And darkness spreads its legs for hate and ignorance.
We are given to a god to put our faith therein,
But to be forgiven, we must first believe in sin.
(To Chorus:)

Verse 4:
I want to live bravely and love without fear.
I want always to feel the wings of grace near.
We all will be Christed when we hear ourselves say
We are that to which we pray.
(To Chorus:)

JUPITER

Tune guitar: **D-A-D-G-B-E**

Words and Music by
JEWEL KILCHER

D.S.℠ al Coda

⊕ *Coda*

Swal - low the moon._____

Swal - low_____

the moon._____

ENTER FROM THE EAST

Words and Music by
JEWEL KILCHER

Moderately slow ♩ = 69

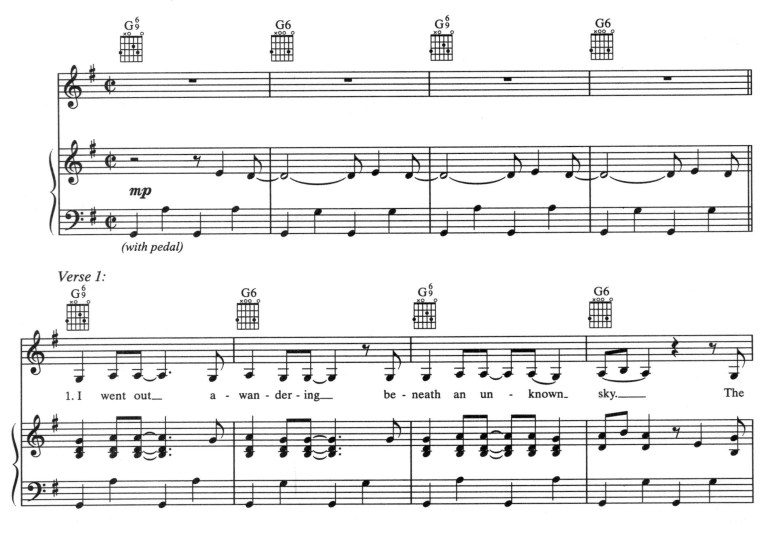

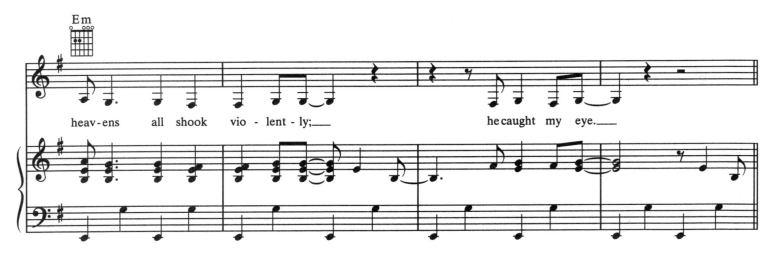

1. I went out___ a-wan-der-ing___ be-neath an un-known_ sky.___ The heav-ens all shook vio-lent-ly;___ he caught my eye.___

Enter From the East - 6 - 1
PF9836

68

Verse 3:
The clock became a bullet hole,
Cruel and unkind.
It hurt me with its second hand,
Alone another night.
(To Chorus:)

Verse 4:
I must have you all to myself;
Feel the full weight of your skin.
I'll hollow out my insides
To place you in.
(To Chorus:)

BARCELONA

Tune guitar: D-A-D-G-B-E

Words and Music by
JEWEL KILCHER

Verse 2:
Super paranoid, I'm blending, I'm blurring, I'm bleeding into the scenery.
Loving someone else is always so much easier,
But I hold myself hostage in the mirror.
But if you could hear the voice in my heart,
It would tell you I'm tired of feeling this way.
God, won't you please hold me?
Release me, show me the meaning of mercy.
Let me loose.
Let me fly.
Let me fly.
Let me fly.
(To Bridge:)

DO YOU

Words and Music by
JEWEL KILCHER

Bridge:

Verse 2:
There's a big man wearing a white suit and patent leather shoes.
He wants to take his monkeys to see the kids at the zoo
'Cause the gypsy on the corner said,
"Hey, Mister! You can't lose!"
And it's your first day at the track, you feel that heat on your back.
We all want to find a way to beat the system,
Find some rhythm in the madness.
(To Chorus 2:)

Chorus 2:
Get down on your knees and pray.
Say, "I'll do whatever you want, God,
Just let me have my way."
Well, will you?
Will you?
(To Bridge:)

Verse 3:
You, with all your cigarettes and cool stares,
Filled with blank glares and loaded regrets,
Just like the girls today with nothing to say.
No more pigtails and pony rides,
They're sophisticated; they sip on lattes
And have their eyes on a bigger prize.
(To Chorus 3:)

LIFE UNCOMMON

Words and Music by
JEWEL KILCHER

Moderately ♩ = 96

Verse 1:

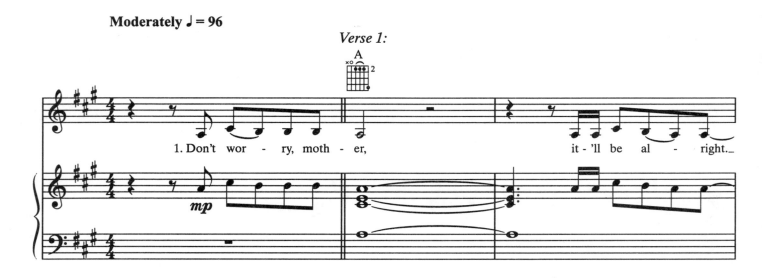

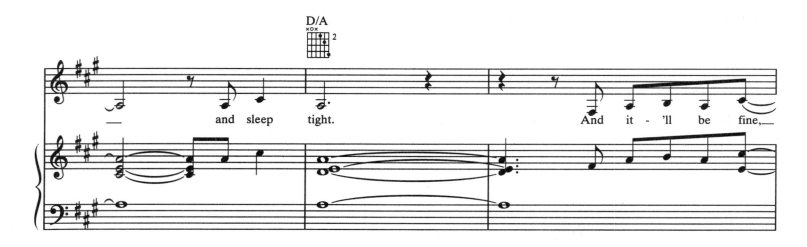

Life Uncommon - 8 - 1
PF9836

Verse 3:
Come on, you unbelievers, move out of the way,
There is a new army coming and we are armed with faith.
To live, we must give.
To live.
(To Chorus:)

ABSENCE OF FEAR

Words and Music by
JEWEL KILCHER

Verse 2:

2. Mus - cle and sin - ew,___ vel - vet and stone.___

D.S.% al Coda

This ves - sel is haunt - ed;___ it creaks and moans.___

⊕ *Coda*

sence of fear. There is___ this hun - ger, this

Bridge:

rest - less - ness___ in - side___ of me. And it knows that you're___ no stran-

Absence of Fear - 6 - 4
PF9836

THIS LITTLE BIRD

Words and Music by
JOHN D. LOUDERMILK